SO-CRV-484

OPEN HIGHWAYS
a diagnostic and developmental reading program

MOVING AHEAD

Helen M. Robinson

Marion Monroe

A. Sterl Artley

Charlotte S. Huck

William A. Jenkins

Ira E. Aaron

Linguistics Advisor, Andrew Schiller

SCOTT, FORESMAN AND COMPANY

CONTENTS

COPYRIGHT © 1968 BY SCOTT, FORESMAN AND COMPANY,
GLENVIEW, ILLINOIS 60025.
All Rights Reserved. Printed in the United States of America.
Regional offices of Scott, Foresman and Company are located in Atlanta,
Dallas, Glenview, Palo Alto, and Oakland, N.J.

Wanted—One Mouse

The Bensons were moving into
an apartment.
The Longs were moving into the
Bensons' house.

Benjy Benson could not take his cat,
Whiskers, with him to the apartment.
And Benjy could not find a home for her.
No one wanted Whiskers.
Then Benjy had an idea.

5

Adapted and reprinted by permission from *Vacation Fun*, © 1964 by Scholastic Maga-
zines, Inc.

Benjy knew that Mrs. Long was coming
to visit the house on Tuesday.
So he went down to the newspaper office.

Benjy said to the man in the office,
"I want to put an ad in the paper."
Benjy took some paper and wrote:

Wanted
One Mouse
Call VI 6-4904

Benjy paid for the ad.
Then he went home to wait for a call.

The next day the telephone rang.
"Hello," said Benjy.

"Do you want a mouse?" asked a voice.
"I have a nice, friendly one for a dollar."

"Good," said Benjy.
"Will you bring the mouse after school
on Tuesday?
I live at 77 Hillside Street."

"See you Tuesday," said the voice.

Benjy got home from school early on
Tuesday.

He sat on the front steps.

Soon a boy came up the walk.

"Is the mouse in that box?" asked Benjy.

The boy said, "Yes. His name is Gray."

Benjy gave the boy a dollar.

He took the box with the mouse.

"Don't be afraid, Gray," said Benjy.
Benjy put the mouse in his pocket.
He walked into the house.
Mrs. Long and his mother were talking
in the front room.

Benjy slipped Gray out of his pocket
as he walked through the room.

9

"Help," cried Mrs. Long.
"There's a mouse in here."
    Benjy ran back into the front room.
The mouse ran out of the room.

    "I'll get Whiskers," said Benjy.
"Mice don't have a chance around her."

    First Benjy went to find Gray.
He put the mouse in the box.
Then he called Whiskers in from the yard.

Benjy went back to the front room.
Mother was talking to Mrs. Long.

"You'll like Whiskers," said Mother.
"She's a good cat."

"I'm sure I will," said Mrs. Long.
"The children will love her, too."

Benjy's plan had worked.
He had found a home for Whiskers.
The next day he put an ad in the paper.

Mice

by Rose Fyleman

I think mice
Are rather nice.

Their tails are long,
Their faces small,
They haven't any
Chins at all.
Their ears are pink,
Their teeth are white,
They run about
The house at night.
They nibble things
They shouldn't touch
And no one seems
To like them much.

But I think mice
Are nice.

12

"Mice" from *Fifty-One New Nursery Rhymes* by Rose Fyleman. Copyright 1932 by Doubleday & Company, Inc. Reprinted by permission of Doubleday & Company, Inc. and the Society of Authors as the literary representative of the Estate of the late Rose Fyleman.

Mr. Dawson Has Cold Feet

One evening Mr. Dawson said to his wife,
"Marjorie, it's cold outside.
Let's get out some extra blankets."

"All right, Donald," said Mrs. Dawson.
"The blankets are in the attic.
Let's get them now."

They went to the attic and got two old
blankets.

13

Adapted from *Mr. Dawson Had a Farm* by R. O. Work, copyright, 1951, by The Bobbs-Merrill Company, Inc., reprinted by permission of the publishers and Betty J. Russell.

Soon the Dawsons went to bed.

"Marjorie," said Mr. Dawson.

"This blanket is very old.

It must have shrunk.

I don't think it will keep me warm."

"It will," said Mrs. Dawson.

So Mr. Dawson closed his eyes.

He felt cold air around his neck.

He pulled the covers up higher.

14

"My feet are cold," said Mr. Dawson.

"Get them under the blanket,"
said Mrs. Dawson.

"It's too short," said Mr. Dawson.

Mrs. Dawson got out of her bed and
pulled the blanket over Mr. Dawson's feet.
Then she went back to bed.

Now Mr. Dawson's feet were warm.
But his neck was cold again.
"My neck's cold," said Mr. Dawson.

"Pull up the blanket," said Mrs. Dawson.

Mr. Dawson pulled the blanket up.
Soon his feet were cold again.
"My feet are cold," he said.

Mrs. Dawson went to the kitchen to fill
a hot-water bottle for Mr. Dawson's feet.
Soon Mr. Dawson went to sleep.

The next morning Mr. Dawson said,
"Now I'll fix that short blanket.
Give me some scissors, a needle,
and some thread."

Mrs. Dawson gave them to him.
Then Mr. Dawson put his blanket on
the table.
He cut a piece off the top of the
blanket and sewed it onto the bottom.

Mr. Dawson went to bed early that night.
Soon he felt cold air around his neck.
So he pulled the covers up higher.
Then his feet were cold.

"My feet are cold," Mr. Dawson said.

"Oh, not again!" said Mrs. Dawson.

All night Mr. Dawson's neck and
feet were cold.
Mrs. Dawson kept tucking him in.
But that didn't seem to help.

The next morning Mr. Dawson cut a
wider piece off the top of the blanket.
He sewed it onto the bottom.

That night Mr. Dawson's neck got cold.
His feet got cold, too.
He said, "Now I'm cold all over."

Mrs. Dawson looked at the blanket.
She said, "It's shorter now than it
was in the beginning."

"Oh, no, it's longer," said Mr. Dawson.
"I've sewed two pieces to the bottom.
I cut them off the top."

"Oh, I see," said Mrs. Dawson.
"Well, here is a scarf for your neck and
a sweater for your feet.
Now you'll be warm."

Mr. Dawson put them on, and then
he went to sleep.

19

The next day Mrs. Dawson went shopping.
She came home with a big package.
She opened the package and pulled out
a very special blanket.
It was ten feet wide and fifteen feet long.

"Oh, Marjorie," said Mr. Dawson.
"That's a fine blanket.
Now we both can get some sleep."

The Hare and the Tortoise

One day the hare said, "I'm the fastest animal in the forest!
No one can beat me.
Who wants to race me to the river?"

"I'll race you," said the tortoise.

"Ha! Ha! Ha!" laughed the hare.
"You're too slow!   You can't beat me!"

"Just let me try," said the tortoise.

And so the hare and the tortoise
began their race to the river.
The tortoise moved along very slowly.
The hare ran very fast.

"There's the river," said the hare.
"It won't take me long to get there now.
The tortoise is far behind me.
I think I'll stop and rest awhile."
So the hare fell asleep under a big tree.

The tortoise slowly walked on.
He did not stop to rest.

At last the hare woke up.
"It's getting dark," said the hare.
"I must hurry and get to the river."
He ran as fast as he could.

The hare saw the tortoise sitting by
the river.

"How did you get here?" asked the
hare.

"I am slow," said the tortoise.
"But I do not stop to rest."

Slow but sure wins the race!

The Little Turtle

by Vachel Lindsay

There was a little turtle.
He lived in a box.
He swam in a puddle.
He climbed on the rocks.

He snapped at a mosquito.
He snapped at a flea.
He snapped at a minnow.
And he snapped at me.

He caught the mosquito.
He caught the flea.
He caught the minnow.
But he didn't catch me.

25

Reprinted with permission of The Macmillan Company from *Collected Poems* by Vachel Lindsay. Copyright 1920 by The Macmillan Company, renewed 1948 by Elizabeth C. Lindsay.

WATER

IF . . .

    It is a warm summer day
and you are sitting by a stream . . .
AND IF . . .

    You look around very, very carefully . . .

    What plants and animals do you think
you would see?
Would they be on the land or in the water?

Some animals and plants always have
to be in water.
Fish cannot live out of water.
Living things of the land need water, too.
Trees need rain to grow.
Deer come to the stream to drink.
In fact, all plants and all animals
need water to live.

Many years ago, men built their homes
beside lakes or rivers.
Then it was easy for men to get water.

Today, many men live a long way
from a river or a lake.
If you live in a city, you turn on a faucet
to get water.
The water from a faucet is still
river water or lake water.
How does the water get to the faucet?

Big pipes carry water from the lake
to the city.
Then smaller pipes bring the water
into your house.

These pictures show some ways that
water is used.

Can you think of other ways
that water is used?

A Green Plant

It was spring in the city.
Miguel sat on the roof every day.
He liked to watch the cars down below.
But he missed living on the old farm.

One day Miguel found a small
plant growing on the roof.
It smelled like a tomato plant.

Miguel thought, "Maybe it will
grow big.
Maybe there will be tomatoes on it."

32

Adapted by special permission from *Jack and Jill* Magazine. © 1967 The Curtis Publishing Company.

Every day Miguel hurried home from
school to see his green plant.
It grew very slowly.
Then the leaves began to turn yellow.

"The plant will die," thought Miguel.
"I wonder what's wrong with it.
I'll ask my teacher."

33

The next day Miguel asked his teacher about the tomato plant.
She gave him a book about plants.
There was a page about a tomato plant.
It showed how the seed must have rich dirt, sunshine, and water to grow.

Next it showed how little flowers come out on the plant.

Last it showed how little green tomatoes grow where the flowers were.

Miguel got a big box on his way home.
He got some rich dirt to fill the box.
Then he hurried up to the roof.

Miguel dug up his plant carefully.
He put the long root into the rich dirt.
That night it rained.

In a week Miguel's plant was
straight and tall.
There were more green leaves on it.

Miguel watched his plant grow.
He put a stick in the box to hold
the plant up.
The plant grew little yellow flowers.
Soon little green tomatoes began to grow
inside the flowers.
Then the yellow flowers died.

Many weeks passed.
The green tomatoes grew bigger and bigger.
The rain helped them grow.
The sun turned them red.
Soon there were many red tomatoes.

Miguel gave his mother some tomatoes.
She cut some up for dinner.
Miguel's family liked the fresh tomatoes.

The next spring Miguel's family helped him plant a garden.
It was a little roof garden in the city.

Tommy

by Gwendolyn Brooks

I put a seed into the ground
And said, "I'll watch it grow."
I watered it and cared for it
As well as I could know.

38

"Tommy" from *Bronzeville Boys and Girls* by Gwendolyn Brooks. Copyright © 1956 by Gwendolyn Brooks Blakely. Reprinted by permission of Harper & Row, Publishers.

One day I walked in my back yard,
And oh, what did I see!
My seed had popped itself right out,
Without consulting me.

The Spy Next Door

Ramsey Lake could not sleep.
First he sat up in his bed.
Then he got up and looked out the window.

Ramsey woke up his two brothers.
"You've got to see this!" he whispered.

"See what?" asked Sid.
"It's night, and everyone is in bed.
There's nothing to see."

"Look at the house next door!"
whispered Ramsey.

No one had lived in the house next to
the Lakes' for a long time.
The doors had big locks on them.
There were boards over all the windows.

The boys went over to their window.
They saw a light in the house next door.
It was shining through the cracks
between the boards.

"Someone's broken into the house!"
said Ramsey.

41

"Hey! The light went out!" said Jason.
"Watch the doors!" said Sid.

A man came out the back door.

"Look! Now he's slipping around the
house!" said Ramsey.
"He could be a robber!   Or even a spy!"

"There he goes," said Jason.

"We'll never get him tonight," said Sid.
"But let's look around tomorrow.
Maybe we'll find out what's going on."

The next day the boys hurried home
from school.

They looked in the house next door.
Everything seemed all right.

"Let's keep a lookout," said Sid.
"The man might come back tonight."

Soon it got dark.
The boys saw many men walk
down the street.
At last, one man went up to the house
next door.

"Well, he's not a robber," said Sid.
"He's got a key to the house."

"Maybe he's a spy," said Ramsey.
"Let's go see what he's doing."

The boys slowly walked up to the house.
They peeked through the window boards.

"I can't see anything!" said Jason.

"Shhhhhh!" said his brothers.

There was a big can under one window.
Jason tried standing on it.
But before he could see anything,
he fell down.
The can rolled away.
It banged on the walk.

Just then the door opened, and
there was the man!

"Why, hello," said the man.
"Do you live near here?"

"N-n-next door," said Ramsey.
"Who — who — who are you?"

"I'm Mr. Collins," said the man.
"I guess we're neighbors.
I'm working on the house after work.
My family is going to move in next week."

"Oh!" said the boys.

"Hope we'll be seeing a lot of you,"
said Mr. Collins.

"Sure," said the boys.
"Well, good-by."

"Good-by, boys,"
said Mr. Collins.

The children started laughing
as they walked back to their house.

"Some robber!" said Sid.
"Some spy!" said Jason.
"I wonder if he has any boys
my age," said Ramsey.

The Mailbox Birdhouse

One weekend a bird built a nest in
Mrs. Rose's mailbox.
On Monday, the mailman, Mr. Oak,
put a letter in the mailbox.
The bird pecked Mr. Oak's finger.

Mr. Oak was very upset.
He went to see Mrs. Rose.

He said, "There's a bird in your mailbox.
It pecked my finger."

Reprinted from *Stories.* © 1967 by The Geneva Press.

Mrs. Rose fixed Mr. Oak's finger.
Then they went to look at the bird.

"Well, well," said Mrs. Rose.
"I must have left the door open."

"That was careless," said Mr. Oak.
"You won't get any mail until that
bird is gone."

Mr. Oak drove away in his truck.

Mrs. Rose went into the house.

She didn't want to make the bird leave.

But she wanted her mail.

So Mrs. Rose put a note on a bag.

It said:

Mailbox is still a birdhouse.
Please put letters in bag.

Mrs. Rose put the bag on the mailbox.

The next morning Mrs. Rose gave
the bird some bread.
Then she looked at the bag.
There was a note from Mr. Oak.
It said:

Bag might get wet.
Letters might get wet, too.
Be smart!
Get rid of the bird!

Mrs. Rose was very sad.
Now she had to make another mailbox.

Later Mrs. Rose put a pot on
the mailbox.
She put a note outside the pot.
It said:

> Mailbox is still a birdhouse.
> Please put letters in pot.

The next morning Mrs. Rose gave the
bird some bugs.
Then she looked in the pot.
There was a note from Mr. Oak.
It said:

> Pot might fall off mailbox.
> Letters would blow away.
> Be smart!
> Get rid of the bird!

Mrs. Rose did not know what to do.

She said, "My new birdhouse is empty, and my mailbox has a bird in it. I wish the bird lived in the birdhouse."

Then Mrs. Rose had an idea. She took the new birdhouse off a tree in the yard. She hung it on the fence next to the mailbox. Then she put a note on it. It said:

Mailbox is still a birdhouse.
Birdhouse is now a mailbox.
Please put letters in here.

The next morning Mrs. Rose gave
the bird some worms.
Then she looked in the birdhouse.
There were three letters and a note.
The note said:

> Birdhouse is high and dry.
> If mailbox can be birdhouse,
> then birdhouse can be mailbox.
> That's smart!
> Good luck to you and the bird!

Mailbox Wren

by Frances Frost

The wren inspects
Her garden house,
Turns up her beak,
And darts to choose

My mailbox gleaming
On its post.
There, her eggs are
Small as stamps, almost.

55

From *The Little Naturalist* by Frances Frost. Illustrated by Kurt Werth. Copyright © 1959 by the Estate of Frances Frost and Kurt Werth. Used by permission of McGraw-Hill Book Company.

Too Many

Willamae Temple was not happy.
She did not want to eat.
Willamae did not like to hear her
mother yelling at Ronnie and Julius.
She did not like to see her sisters
fighting all the time.

Willamae thought, "I'll go outside.
It's quiet at my tree in the park."

Willamae went to her tree.
A little girl was sitting under it.
Willamae did not like to have
someone sitting under her tree.

Willamae said, "Why are you
sitting under my tree?
It's been mine for two years."

"I didn't know this was your tree,"
said the girl.
"It's a nice, cool spot on a hot day.
We can both sit under this big tree."
The girl moved over.

Willamae sat down under the tree.

She thought, "That girl is trying to
sweet-talk my tree away from me.
She thinks she's something in those
new clothes.
I'd better watch her!"

"My name is Geraldine," said the girl.
"I was getting lonely.
I don't have any sisters or brothers."

"Who needs them!" said Willamae.
"I'll give you six of mine."

The two girls talked for a long time.
Willamae began to feel better.
And she liked Geraldine better, too.

The girls met under their special
tree every day.

Willamae thought, "I wish I could
be Geraldine.
She doesn't have any brothers and
sisters who fight all the time.
And she doesn't have to hear a lot
of yelling."

Then one Saturday the Temple family
was going to the baseball game.
But Willamae had a very bad cold.
Her mother would not let her go out.

Soon Dad and the children left for
the baseball park.
Mother fixed two hamburgers for
Willamae.
Then Mother went to take a nap.

Willamae watched TV.

She thought, "Julius would like this cartoon."

Then came a circus show.

Willamae thought, "The twins would like this show.
They like clowns."

The day passed slowly.
Willamae tried to read.
But she could not read all of the words.
There was no one to help her.

"It's too quiet," thought Willamae.
"It's nice to have a little quiet.
But I've had enough for today.
Maybe Geraldine doesn't have
so much fun alone.
I guess I'm lucky to have brothers
and sisters.
I can always go sit under my tree when
I want to be alone."

Frog Sitters

"Boys," said Mother.
"You'll have a new sitter tonight.
Polly is a high-school girl."

"Oh, no!" said Sam and Tom.
"They're no fun.
They just talk on the phone."

The doorbell rang.
Mother opened the door for Polly.
Polly came in with a box in her hand.

Reprinted from *Stories*. © 1960 by W. L. Jenkins.

Soon Mother and Father left.
Tom asked Polly, "What's in the box?"

"Dan's in there," said Polly.
"I thought you would like to see him."
Polly opened the box.
A frog jumped out.

Polly threw a bug up into the air.
Dan jumped up and got it.
The boys threw bugs up into the air, too.

Soon it was time for the boys to take their baths.

Sam said, "Let's hurry!
Maybe we'll have time to play a game
before we go to bed."

Tom and Sam took their baths as
fast as they could.
Then they ran to find Polly.

Polly was reading in the front room.
Dan was sitting at her feet.

65

The children played a game.
Then Polly asked, "Where's Dan?
We forgot to put him back in his box."

"We'll find him," said Tom.
Everyone looked for Dan.
They looked under the chairs and tables.
But no one could find Dan.

Polly said, "You boys must go to bed.
Dan will show up later.
Then you can bring him to my house."

The boys went to brush their teeth.

Tom yelled, "Polly, look!

The water is still in the tub.

And there's Dan!

He thinks he's in a pool of water.

That sponge is like a lily pad!"

They all laughed and laughed.

Then Polly put Dan back into his box.

The boys washed the tub.

At last the boys were ready for bed.
Sam said, "We had fun tonight, Polly.
Maybe you can sit with us again."

"I hope so," said Polly.
"You can watch Dan for me next time."

"OK," laughed Tom.
"You can be our sitter.
And we'll be Dan's sitter."

Both boys said, "We'll be frog sitters!"

Frogs

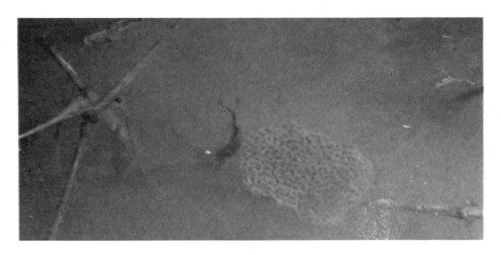

Here are frog eggs.
There are tadpoles in the eggs.

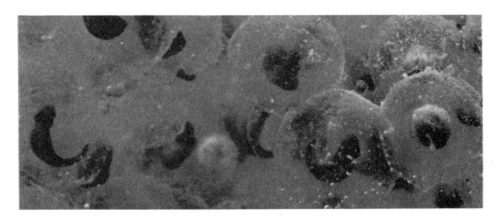

This is how tadpoles look in the eggs.
The eggs hatch in 4 to 15 days.

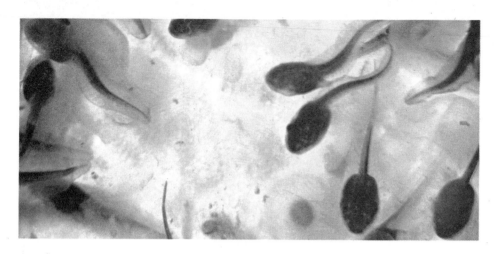

The tadpoles are out of the eggs.
Tadpoles are black and white or
brown and yellow.

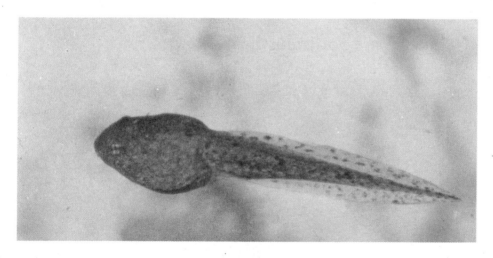

A tadpole looks like a tiny fish.
Some tadpoles are 6 to 7 inches long.
And some tadpoles are very small.

The tadpole begins to grow back legs.

Its body grows larger.

Its tail grows larger.

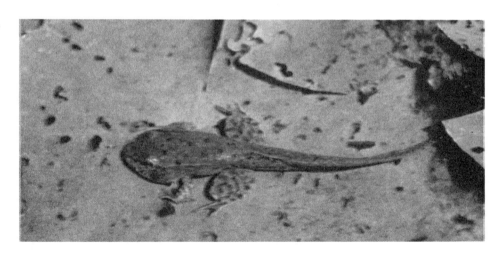

The tadpole has front legs now.

Its body grows larger.

But its tail gets smaller.

Now the tadpole is a frog.

He can live in water and on land.

Some frogs live for 15 years.

A Frog Went A-Courting

A frog went a-courting he did ride,

Hmm hmm, hmm hmm.

A frog went a-courting he did ride

With the sword and pistol by his side,

Hmm hmm, hmm hmm.

He rode up to Miss Mouse's door,
Hmm hmm, hmm hmm.
He rode up to Miss Mouse's door
Where he had never been before,
Hmm hmm, hmm hmm.

He says, "Miss Mouse won't you marry me?"
Hmm hmm, hmm hmm.
He says "Miss Mouse won't you marry me?"
"No, not without Uncle Rat will agree,"
Hmm hmm, hmm hmm.

Uncle Rat went a-running down to town,
Hmm hmm, hmm hmm.
Uncle Rat went a-running down to town
To get his niece a wedding gown,
Hmm hmm, hmm hmm.

The frog would laugh and shake his sides,
Hmm hmm, hmm hmm.
The frog would laugh and shake his sides
To think Miss Mouse would be his bride,
Hmm hmm, hmm hmm.

Laugh Time

"Maybe Mrs. Parks doesn't want
to look at your frog, Sam."

Copyright © 1967 Highlights for Children, Inc., Columbus, Ohio.

Sweet Porridge

Once upon a time there was a poor girl named Liza.
She lived alone with her mother.
They had nothing to eat.
So the child went into the woods to find something to eat.

Liza met an old woman in the woods.
The old woman liked Liza.
She gave Liza a magic pot.

"Sweet Porridge" adapted from *Grimm's Fairy Tales*.

The old woman told Liza, "You
must say COOK, LITTLE POT, COOK.
Then the pot will cook good, sweet
porridge for you.
Eat all you want.
Then say STOP, LITTLE POT, STOP.
And the pot will stop cooking."

Liza took the pot home.
She showed her mother how to make
porridge.

One day Liza left the house.
Her mother wanted to use the magic pot.
She said, "COOK, LITTLE POT, COOK."

The pot cooked.
Liza's mother ate and ate.
Then she wanted the pot to stop.
But she did not know the magic words.
So the pot went on cooking.
The porridge ran over the pot's edge.
It ran all over the kitchen floor.

Soon the porridge ran out of the house.
It ran down the street.

The people in town were unhappy.
No one knew the magic words
to stop the pot.

At last Liza came back.

She saw the porridge all over town.

Liza cried, "STOP, LITTLE POT, STOP."

The pot stopped cooking.

Everyone wanted to go home.

They could not get through the porridge.

There was only one thing to do.

They all ate their way back home.

A Baseball Player

"There's nothing to do," said Pam.
"Let's go to the park and play baseball."

Mary said, "You know we can't.
The boys won't let us play."

"Maybe they will," said Pam.
"They might need more players."
So the girls went to the park.

Mary and Pam ran into the park.
Al yelled, "Get out of here!
We don't want any girls around!"

Pam said, "We can play.
We can play as well as you can."
But the girls knew they could not stay.
The boys would never let them play now.
So the girls left the park.

Mary said, "Let's go meet the new girl in our building.
Maybe she can come out and play with us."

They went to the new girl's door.
Pam rang the bell.
The new girl answered the door.

Pam said, "I'm Pam, and this is Mary.
Can you come out to play?"

"Hi, I'm Samantha," the girl said.
"Just call me Sam.
Come in and sit down.
I'll ask my mom if I can go out."

Pam and Mary sat down on the couch.
Pam said, "I've got an idea."
She whispered into Mary's ear.

Sam came back into the room.
The girls told her their idea.
Sam ran and got a cap and baseball mitt.
She pinned her hair under the cap.

"That's great, Sam!" cried Mary.
"Let's see if you can fool the boys.
Pam and I will walk as far as
the park gate with you."

Sam went into the park alone.

Al saw Sam and yelled to her,

"Do you want to play?

We need another man over here.

I'm Al.   What's your name?"

"Sam," said Samantha.

She ran to left field.

Soon Sam caught the ball.

She threw it to first base.   Out!

Al's team needed one more out to win.

Then Sam caught a high fly.
Everyone clapped for Sam.
That was the last out.

Al yelled, "What a player!
Sam will have to play with us tomorrow."

Sam smiled.
She said, "I'd love to play tomorrow.
I have two friends who want to play, too."

Sam took off her cap.
Her hair fell down.
The boys were surprised.

Pam and Mary ran into the park.
They said, "We showed you boys!
You think only boys can play baseball.
Girls can play, too."

Al said, "Maybe some girls can play.
Let's all play tomorrow.
We'll see if you girls can play
a good game more than once."

Make a Baseball Game

You will need:

scissors
sock
ruler and pencil
dried beans or buttons   tagboard
needle and thread   hanger
felt pen or crayon   tape

First make a bean-bag baseball.

Draw a line four inches from the toe of a sock.

Cut along the line.

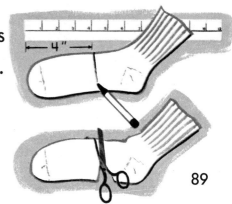

89

Draw a funny face on the front
of the bean bag.

Then fill the bag about three-fourths full
of buttons or dried beans.

Now turn in the open edges
and sew the bag closed.

Next make the baseball field.

Cut out the circles
on the tagboard.

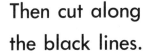

Then cut along
the black lines.

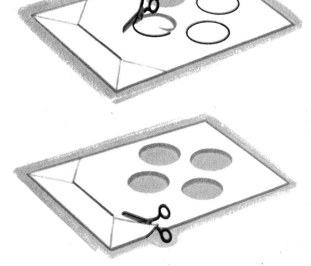

Bend the board back
on the red line.
Put it over the hanger.

Tape the back.

Write **home, first, second,**
and **third** by the bases.
Follow the picture to see
where to write them.

Last, play ball!

Bingo

Bingo was a lazy boy.
He never wanted to work.
All he wanted to do was sleep or watch TV.

"Son," said Bingo's mother.
"Pick your things up off the floor.
Don't be so lazy."

Bingo thought, "Every day Mom tells
me that!
How can I pick up my things and not
work too hard?"

Bingo thought and thought.

"A magnet," cried Bingo.

"Maybe I can use a magnet to pick up
my things.

But a magnet won't pick up my clothes.

It will only pick up iron or steel."

Then Bingo had an idea.

He said, "I'll put big, steel paper clips
on all my clothes.

Then the magnet will pick them up."

Bingo got a box of big paper clips.

He put clips on all of his clothes
on the floor.

93

First Bingo ran to the
east corner of his room.
He picked up his blue shirt
with his magnet.

Next he picked up
his black pants in the
west corner.

He picked up his red socks
in the north corner.

Last, he picked up
his green cap in the
south corner.

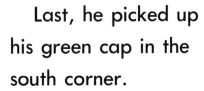

Bingo was tired of running back and forth.
He fell on the bed.

"This is too hard," he said.
"I want to rest while I'm picking up
my clothes.
How can I watch TV and keep
my room clean?"

Lazy Bingo thought and thought.
At last he got another idea.

Bingo got a fishing rod out of the closet.
He tied the big magnet to the end of
the fishing line.
Then Bingo threw the magnet over
to the south corner of the room.
He moved it a little to the left.
Then he moved it a little to the right.

The magnet caught the large
paper clip that was inside his red shirt.
Bingo reeled in the shirt.

Then Bingo reeled in more clothes.
"It works!" cried Bingo.
"Now I can keep my clothes picked up
and have fun doing it."

Bingo's mother never had to tell
him to pick up his clothes again.
He always had a clean room.

Danger in the Dark

It was raining hard.
Toby and Polly were hurrying home.

"Toby," said Polly.
"The creek water is getting higher.
Will it get up to our house?"

"Fraidycat!" yelled Toby.
"It never has before."

Polly ran to the dark house.
She called, "Mom, we're home."
No one, answered.

Adapted by special permission from *Jack and Jill* Magazine. © 1965 The Curtis Publishing Company.

Polly opened the door.
She turned on the lights.

"Nobody's home," she said.
"Here's a note from Mom on the table.
It says she's at Grandmother's house.
Mom will be back for dinner."

"Okay," said Toby.
"I'm going to feed the cows now.
You call Mom and tell her we're home."

"Don't leave me alone," cried Polly.

"Fraidycat!" yelled Toby.
He hurried out to the barn.

Polly tried to call her mother.

"Hello! Hello!" she said.

There was no sound on the telephone.

Then the lights went out.

Polly dropped the telephone.

She pushed the light switch.

But the lights did not go on.

"Help!" called Toby from outside.

Polly put on her raincoat.

She ran out into the pouring rain.

"Toby, where are you?" called Polly.
She looked around the dark yard.
She saw Toby in a pool of brown water.
He was hanging onto the fence.

"I ran after a cow," Toby said.
"The creek came up too fast.
It washed the feedbin over on me.
My leg is caught under it.
Don't come any closer.
You'll fall into the water."

Polly found a rope and tied it to her.
She tied the other end to the fence.
Then she waded into the water.
Polly let the rope out a little.
Slowly she got closer to Toby.

Polly pushed on the feedbin.
It slid to one side, and Toby was free.
He held onto Polly.
And they waded through the water.

The children got to the porch.

Toby's leg was hurting.

Polly took off Toby's raincoat and boots.

Then she took hers off.

They went into the house.

Toby sat on the couch.

Polly found a flashlight in the desk.

She got Toby's pajamas and robe for him.

She put a pillow and blanket on the couch.

Then Polly changed her clothes.

"I think I'll start dinner," said Polly.
"I'll make a big pot of hot soup for you.
Mom may not get home 'til late."

Toby was very tired.
"Polly," he said.
"I'll never call you a fraidycat again.
Not after what you did tonight.
You're very brave."

A Rain Riddle

Three large ladies heard it thunder.
Three large ladies all got under
One small umbrella, or tried to get.
Why didn't the three large ladies get wet?

It didn't rain.

Reprinted from *Riddles, Riddles Everywhere*. Copyright © 1964 by Ennis Rees. By permission of Abelard-Schuman, Ltd. All Rights Reserved.

One Little Drum

Johnny looked in the store window.
He saw a drum that he liked.
Johnny went inside the store.

He asked the storekeeper, "How
much is that drum in the window?"

"It's ten dollars," said the man.
"It's a nice drum.
The drumsticks go with it."

Adapted from *One Little Drum,* Copyright © 1958 by Margaret Hodges, by permission
of Follett Publishing Company and McIntosh and Otis, Inc.

"I want that drum," said Johnny.
"I have a dollar now.
Maybe I can work for the other money.
Will you save the drum for me?"

"All right," said the man.
"Write your name on this paper."

Johnny wrote his name on the paper.
He gave the man his dollar.
Then Johnny went home.

Johnny asked his mother how he could
earn some money.

"You can wash the dishes," she said.
"Dad will pay you a dime each day.
But you have to do your other work, too."

Johnny worked very hard.
He saved his dimes.
At last he had five dollars.
He took them to the storekeeper.

Johnny wanted to earn his last four
dollars quickly.

"I'll have a magic show," he thought.
"Billy, Sue, Judy, and Joe will come.
I can charge them ten cents each.
Maybe some other kids will come, too.
I'll make the tickets right now."

Johnny made his tickets.

Johnny got a book at the library.

It had magic tricks in it.

Johnny practiced many tricks.

By Saturday he knew six tricks.

And he had sold seven tickets to his show.

On Saturday Johnny gave his show.

All the children had a good time.

Johnny's mother served cookies and
milk to the children.

The next day Sue's mother called.
"Hello," she said to Johnny.
"Sue is going to have a party.
She wants you to do your magic show.
How much do you charge?"

"Ten cents each," said Johnny.

"That's fine," said Sue's mother.
"You can come next Saturday at 3:00."

Johnny gave his show.
And his money began to grow again.

At last Johnny had all of his money.
He took it to the music store.

Johnny looked in the store window.
He saw a drum that he liked.
It was not like the other drum.
It was bigger and came with a stand.

Johnny went into the store.

"Hello," said Johnny.
"I brought the rest of the money."
He gave the man the money.
The man gave Johnny his drum.

"How much is that drum in the
window?" asked Johnny.

"Twenty dollars," said the man.

"Put it away for me," said Johnny.
"I'll start earning the money today."

Pictionary for Moving Ahead

Words for People

mailman

> The mailman brings letters.

man

> When a boy grows up
> he is a man.

men

> When boys grow up
> they are men.

people

> Men, women, and children
> are people.

player

A baseball team has nine
players on it.

woman

When a girl grows up
she is a woman.

women

When girls grow up
they are women.

Words for Places

apartment

An apartment is a part of
a building where people live.

attic

An attic is the space below
the roof and above the
other rooms of a house.

barn

A barn is a building for
farm animals and a place
for storing hay and grain.
See the picture for **farm**.

city

A city is a large town with many people living in it and with many tall buildings.

creek

A creek is smaller than a stream. See the picture for **river**.

farm

A farm is where animals and things to eat are raised.

barn   house

garden

A garden is a piece of
ground where vegetables
or flowers grow.

lake

A lake is water with
land all around it.

office

An office is where some
people work.

place

A place is where a person
or thing is.

river

A river is a large stream
of running water.

stream

creek

river

stream

A stream is smaller
than a river.
See the picture for **river**.

Words for Animals

animal

An animal is any living thing
that can feel and move.

cow

A cow is a farm animal
that gives milk.

deer

A deer is a wild animal
that lives in the forest.

flea

A flea is a very small bug
with no wings.

hare

A hare is like a rabbit, but bigger.

minnow

A minnow is a little fish.

mosquito

A mosquito is a kind of bug.

tortoise

A tortoise is a kind of turtle
that lives on land.

turtle

A turtle has a hard shell.
Many turtles live in water.

Words for Things

building

A building is something with walls and a roof. A school is a building.

cartoon

A cartoon is a picture showing something funny.

cent

A cent is one penny.

couch

A couch is a long seat with arms and a back.

dime

A dime is worth ten cents or ten pennies.

dollar

A dollar is worth ten dimes or one hundred cents or one hundred pennies.

faucet

A faucet is what we turn on to get water.

feedbin

A feedbin is what a
farmer puts food in
to feed animals.

flashlight

A flashlight is a light
you can carry with you
and turn on and off.

lily pad

A lily pad is the leaf
of a water-lily plant.

lily pad

magnet

A magnet is a piece of iron or steel that pulls to it other things made of iron or steel.

pipe

A pipe is a tube through which water or gas flows.

rod

A rod is a thin, straight piece of metal or wood.

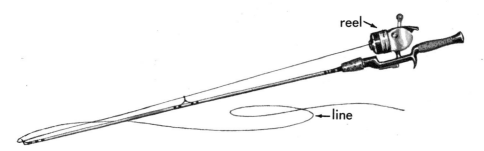

reel

line

sponge

A sponge holds much water and is good for washing things.

thing

A thing is something you can hear, smell, touch, or taste.

Acknowledgments

Book cover and title page designed by Bradford/Cout Graphic Design.

The illustrations in this book are by:

Suzy Moore, pages 5-11
Rod Ruth, pages 12, 26-27, 55
Justin Wager, pages 13-20
Pat Dypold, pages 21-24
Sid Jordan, page 25
Jack White, pages 28-31, 89-91
Marilyn Hirsch, pages 32-37
Carl Carter, pages 38-39
Jack Smith, pages 40-47

Dezso Csanady, pages 48-54
Francisco Sanchez, pages 56-62
Jack Wallen, pages 63-68, 92-97
Phoebe Moore, pages 74-75
John Magine, pages 76, 105
Star Bellei, pages 77-81
Tony Paul, pages 82-88
Chuck Mitchell, pages 98-104
Joe Rogers, pages 106-114

The photographs in this book are courtesy of:

H. Armstrong Roberts, pages 29, 30 (right), 31 (right)
Fundamental Photographs, page 30 (top)
Ward Sharrer, Black Star, page 30 (left)
Charles Phelps Cushing, page 32 (top)
Donald Stebbing, page 31 (left)
Janet L. Stone from National Audubon Society, page 69 (top)
C. G. Maxwell from National Audubon Society, page 69 (bottom)
William Jahoda from National Audubon Society, page 70 (top)
Stephen Collins from National Audubon Society, pages 70 (bottom),
    71 (top)
W. Hassler, courtesy of the American Museum of Natural History,
    page 71 (bottom)
Robert Erwin from National Audubon Society, page 72